Horizons

Van's Scarecrow

Horizons
Phonics and Reading K
Reader 4

Author: Pollyann O'Brien, M.A.

Editor: Alan L. Christopherson, M.S.

Illustrations: Brian Ring
                Karen Eubanks, B.A.
                Dawn Tessier, B.A.

Alpha Omega Publications • Chandler, Arizona

Printed in the United States of America

ISBN 0-7403-0144-6

2

A Note to Teachers and Parents

The Horizons Kindergarten Phonics Readers are to be used as a companion to the Horizons Kindergarten Phonics Student Workbooks. For each lesson in the Student Workbooks there is a corresponding story in the Readers. The story will illustrate and demonstrate the primary concept of the lesson. Most kindergarten students should not be expected to read these stories independently. The stories include a mixture of simple short-vowel words and more complex multi-syllable or long-vowel words. The teacher or parent should read the stories to the student, pausing where appropriate, to allow the student to sound out and read the words they have covered in the lessons. As the student's vocabulary increases, the teacher or parent is encouraged to repeat the Reader stories in a cyclic fashion. For example; on the day "x" is covered (Lesson 26) both the "x" story and the "short a" story (Lesson 1) can be read.

It is important to ask questions both before and after reading the story. Talk about things to look for or to expect in the story based upon the title or the illustrations. Comprehension questions are included at the end of each story beginning with Lesson 27.

The ability to sound out and read words varies with each individual student. They are in the early stages of learning a skill that they will continue to develop for the rest of their lives. So, have fun, enjoy the stories and keep in mind that it is not necessary that every student sound out and read every word.

Table of Contents

VAN'S SCARECROW

Van was in the fourth grade. He had joined Boy Scout Troop #18. Van had lots of things to learn. The boys had to know plenty before they could get their merit badges.

Van wanted to make a garden to earn his merit badge. He would fix the ground and grow some vegetables. When the ground was ready, the seeds were sown into long rows. He planted corn, beets, beans, carrots, and potatoes. Before long he was able to count the green sprouts in each row.

One day Van took the Boy Scout leader out to the garden to show him the new sprouts. When they got there, Van said, "Oh, no. Half of my sprouts are gone."

Just then they heard, "Caw, Caw, Caw."

The scout leader said, "Van, that old crow was the one who took your corn. Let us fix him. I will help you put up a scarecrow. Then you will have a garden and it will not be stolen."

"Good idea," said Van. "I am going to tie a bell to the scarf on the scarecrow. When the wind blows the scarf a bit, the crow will hear the sound and be scared away."

What club did Van join?
What was he going to do to earn his merit badge?
What happened to the sprouts?
What did Van do about it?

JAYS

The jay birds are part of the crow family. The blue jays have more color than the others birds. Some may be gray or have clay colors. The head has a crown with tall feathers. Jays have shiny black tail feathers.

The jays make loud noises. Many times, you can hear them before you can see them.

In the summertime, jays find acorns. They bury them for the winter. They can always dig down into the dirt and dig up their acorns. No one can tell how they can find them.

The jays like to tease. They tease dogs. They tease cats. They steal their food.

Sometimes a jay will tease the ants in the anthills. The ants get all over the jay. Then the jay will fly fast and drop the ants away from their hills.

Jays come to the campers' tents to steal food the campers may have left out or may have thrown away. They also eat insects and spiders from the hay. They will steal eggs and baby birds from other nests.

Jays are often called "meatbirds" or "camp robbers."

To what family do jays belong?
What do the jays have on their heads?
What do jays find in the summertime?
What are jays often called?

THE DUMP TRUCK

Paul was hauling a load of junk to the dump. He was driving the truck at dawn.

A red auto passed Paul on the road. It was going too fast. The auto hit a curve and spun into a ditch.

Paul put his foot on the brake. He came to a quick stop. He helped the driver out of the auto. The driver was not hurt, but the auto looked bad.

The driver said, "Thanks for your help.

It was my fault. I was going too fast. I do not think I can get my auto out of the ditch though."

Paul said, "I will haul my junk to the dump. It is just a short jaunt. Then I can haul your car to a shop to be fixed. Your auto is not ready for the dump."

"Thanks, again," said the driver. "You are a good scout."

Where was Paul going with his truck?
What passed him on the road?
What happened when the auto hit the curve?
How did Paul help?

THE NEW STEW

Drew watched Mom as she cooked. "What are you making, Mom?" he asked. "It smells so good."

"This is a new stew," said Mom.

Drew watched as Mom threw in some more meat chunks and three carrots. Then she threw in some onions, potatoes and corn.

Drew saw Mom as she screwed the cover on the cooker.

In a few minutes, Drew asked, "Is the new stew ready, Mom?"

Mom said, "The stew has to

brew for two hours. You can go
and play for now. Then you can
come back and have something
new to chew on."

What was Mom doing?
What did she put in the cooker?
How long did she have to cook it?
What did Drew do while the stew was cooking?

THE COWBOY

Troy is a cowboy. He has a pony he calls "Roy". Troy was ten years old when he started to ride horseback.

Troy puts on a big brown cowboy hat. He enjoys putting it on his head and prancing around the yard. He has a red and white cowboy shirt. His cowboy pants and chaps are brown. He has boots to match. It is a joy to see Troy ride his pony, Roy.

He can join the other cowboys and toil with them. Troy likes to ride Roy while he is working or going for a ride.

Who is Troy?
What does he call his pony?
When did Troy start to ride?
What does he wear?

SHAW'S CAMPING TRIP

This was the day Shaw was to go camping. Shaw got up at dawn to fix the camping stuff. He had to crawl under the steps to get the tent. He had to haul the box of camp-cooking pots and pans to the truck. Then he got the food packed.

Shaw met Buck, an Indian, at the teepee. Buck was going to show Shaw how the Indians camped and hunted a long time ago.

An Indian lady had her shawl around her neck and arms. She gave Shaw some food to take with them.

"Thanks," said Shaw. "Buck and I will have more good food."

Buck had his dog, Paw-jaw, with him. Buck said, "I call my dog "Paw-jaw" because he has big paws and a big jaw. He will be a help to find tracks."

Paw-jaw wagged his tail. Shaw patted Paw-jaw's head.

"This will be a good camping trip," said Shaw. "I will learn a lot from Buck and Paw-jaw."

What did Shaw have to get under the steps?
What did he have to haul to the truck?
What was Buck going to show Shaw how to do?
Why did Buck call his dog "Paw-jaw"?

MONEY

Bobby dumped his piggy bank on the table. He said, "Uncle Bill, please help me count my money."

Uncle Bill put some coins on the table. He began to show Bobby how much money he had in his piggy bank.

Uncle Bill said, "Bobby, can you find one penny?"

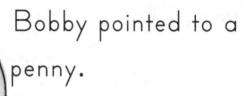

Bobby pointed to a penny.

"Now," said Uncle Bill, "can you find four more pennies and put them here?"

Bobby pushed the coins around and put them where Uncle Bill had pointed. He counted: ONE, TWO, THREE, FOUR, FIVE.

Uncle Bill said, "Now find one nickel."

Bobby pushed the coins around. He found one nickel.

Uncle Bill said, "Good job, Bobby. Now you have a nickel and it is the same as five pennies. So how much money is a nickel and five pennies together? You can count them. Start with the nickel."

Bobby took the nickel and said, "Five." Then he went on and counted the pennies. "Six, seven, eight, nine, ten."

Uncle Bill said, "You have four more pennies. Count all of it."

Bobby started with the nickel again. He said, "Five for the nickel, then six, seven, eight, nine, ten, and then four more pennies. That would be eleven, twelve, thirteen, fourteen cents in my piggy bank. Thanks, Uncle Bill, for helping me."

Where did Bobby keep his money?
How much money is one penny?
How much money is one nickel?
How much money did Bobby have in his bank?

THE CLOWN

"OUCH", shouted Howey, the clown. "How can I keep a smile on my face now? I fell over my big feet three times."

"Why not get on your brown cow. She can take you all over town. Then you will not have to walk," said Troy.

Sammy jumped on the cow. He smiled a wide smile. The crowd shouted, "Good job, Howey!"

Howey rode the cow down to the bed of flowers. The cow

walked into a spray of water. Howey got a shower.

"Move it! Move it!" shouted Howey. "I need a towel."

The cow trotted to the tower with Howey on her back. A big dog was there. He let out a big growl. The cow jumped. Howey fell off. It was all part of the act. The crowd laughed

and howled. Howey stood up with his hands in the air. He gave the crowd a big bow down to his feet. He liked to hear the crowd laugh and howl.

Who was Howey?
What was his trouble at first?
What did Howey ride?
What happened to him?
What did the crowd do?

THE FAWN

A fawn is a baby deer. As soon as a fawn is born it can stand. Ask your mother how old you were when you learned to stand without help.

The mother deer is called a "doe". She takes good care of her fawn.

The fawn is brown or tan with white spots. The color makes it hard for a man to see the fawn. The fawn's fur blends in with the trees and dense shrubs.

When the fawn is about three months old, it is weaned. It starts to eat grass and twigs. The mother deer stays with her fawn for about a year. By then, the fawn is

strong so it can run with the herd. Ask your mother how old you will be when you can be on your own.

Only male deer can grow horns. The horns start to grow when the male fawn is about nine months old.

What is a fawn?
What color is a fawn?
How old is it when it is weaned?
How old is a male fawn when the horns start to grow?

THE WINNER

Claude came home like a grouch. "I never win," he said.

"What is the trouble?" asked Gramps.

"I strike out every time I am up to bat," Claude said. "I do not ever get to sprawl into first base."

"You need to fix your thoughts," said Gramps. "You need to say to yourself: I CAN DO IT. I CAN DO IT. I WILL HIT THE BALL. I AM A WINNER."

"Sure, that is easy for you to say, Gramps. You are already good," said Claude. "I am a squawk!"

"Woops" said Gramps. "What were you going to say?"

"Oh, oh," said Claude. "I will do it again. I CAN DO IT. I WILL HIT THE BALL. I AM A WINNER—I AM NOT A SQUAWK."

"That is better," said Gramps. "Let us go out and hit some balls. Say it once more, Claude."

"I am a winner. I will hit the ball."

Gramps threw three balls
for Claude to hit.

GOOD ONE! GOOD
ONE! GOOD ONE! Claude
was sure he was a winner
now. He felt like a winner.

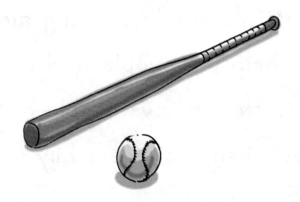

How did Claude feel when he came home?
What did he tell Gramps?
What did Gramps tell Claude to do?
What did Claude keep saying?

THE TOY STORE

Toys! Toys! Toys! This store has as many toys as ten other toy stores put together.

Mr. Choy owns the toy store. He employs fifteen people to help run the store. He employs people to put toys on the shelves. He employs young men and women to help the people find the toys they want. He employs people to take the money when customers buy the toys they want.

The little boys and girls come in to look at the toys. They have so many choices. One boy liked a red truck. He turned the wheels. The wheels made a funny sound. "I think these wheels need oil," said Roy.

Mr. Choy said, "Let me look at that truck. You are right. These wheels do need oil."

Roy asked, "Will you please oil the wheels, Mr. Choy? This is just the truck I want."

Mr. Choy put some oil on the wheels. "It works fine now," he said. "You will enjoy the choice you have made. This is a fine truck."

Who is Mr. Choy?
Why does he employ so many people?
What was wrong with the truck?
How did Mr. Choy fix the truck?

A HOT DAY IN JULY

It was the first part of July and school had been out for a month. It was one of those very hot days. No one could deny that it was the hottest day of the year. Some people joked and said it was so hot you could fry an egg on the sidewalk. The sky was a beautiful blue with fluffy white clouds. The birds would fly to a nearby birdbath and take a sip of water. Then they would splash water all over while they took their baths.

Joey and Sly wanted to do something that was different. It was too hot to do much of anything. "I think what we need to do is to pry ourselves out of this house and go swimming," said Sly. "The water at the lake is probably a little warmer than it usually is, but it will be better than nothing."

"I can not deny that," said Joey. "Let us be on our way. I think we should take Buffy with us. I know our dog likes to swim as much as we do. He needs to cool off, too."

The boys hopped on their bikes with Buffy running at their sides. When they got to the lake, Buffy was the first one to take a flying leap right into the water. He made a big splash. The boys were soaked with water before they had a chance to get off of their bikes.

Sly laughed, "That fuzzy dog is funny. Here it was our idea to get cool, but Buffy beat us to it."

Why did the boys want to go swimming?
How did they get to the lake?
Who got to the lake first?
What did Buffy do?

THE CANARY

The canary is one of the most loved pet birds. People enjoy hearing them sing their lively songs. Many people keep them in their homes in large cages so they do not fly away.

When canaries are in the wild, they prefer to nest in small trees and bushy shrubs. The male chooses the nest-site and brings the tiny twigs and tall grass stems to make the nest. When it is all in the right place, it is the female who builds the nest. She makes a neat, cup-shaped nest of the many twigs and tall grass stems. The nest is held together with white vegetable down. The inside of the nest is lined with feathers, hair, and wool.

The female lays three to five eggs. The male feeds her during the time she sets on the eggs. Both parents take turns bringing food to the baby canaries. The babies feed mostly on soft, half-ripe seeds.

If you keep a canary at home, you should be sure to keep its cage clean. It should be large enough so the bird can fly around a bit. They eat mostly canary food. Canaries also need to have fresh green food, too. Be sure they have plenty of water every day.

Why do most people enjoy having a canary as a pet?
Which one chooses the nest-site and builds the twigs and stems?
Which one builds the nest?
How many eggs do female canaries usually lay?

BENNY BLY,
THE CIRCUS MONKEY

Benny Bly was a very smart monkey. He did tricks in the circus.

Mr. Sandy was Benny's trainer. He trained Benny to do new tricks every day. Mr. Sandy gave Benny his own tiny bedroom. Benny had his tiny pants and shirts just like a tiny boy.

Benny liked to hear the crowd clap. They clapped when he did his tricks on the bars and swings. Mr. Sandy would give a snap with his fingers and Benny would do another trick.

One day Mr. Sandy snapped his fingers. Benny would not do his tricks. He would not even try. "Benny Bly, you are just being silly," said Mr. Sandy.

Benny stuck out his tongue. He made silly faces. He pulled on his ears. He opened his mouth and yawned.

Mr. Sandy was angry. The crowd wanted to see Benny do his tricks. They did not want him to act silly.

Mr. Sandy said, "OK, Benny Bly. You just sit there and act silly. I will get Dolly to do your act."

Mr. Sandy gave a snap of his fingers and Dolly did the tricks. The crowd clapped for her. Benny saw the crowd clapping for Dolly. He began to cry.

Then Benny stopped crying. He clapped his hands. He gave a snap of his fingers just like Mr. Sandy did. Benny jumped up and down. He began to do his tricks. He was sorry he had been so silly. The crowd clapped and howled when Benny did his tricks. He did a very good act.

Who was Benny Bly?
Where did he do his tricks?
Who was Mr. Sandy?
When Benny was silly, what did he do?
When Benny was good, what did he do?

WOOLEY

Brad had a pet lamb called "Wooley". When the lamb was born, he was too small to stay with the sheep herd. Brad fed him his milk from a baby bottle. At first, Brad held him in his arms to feed him. The kids said he looked like Brad's baby.

Soon the lamb was too big for Brad to hold him in his arms. Brad hung Wooley's bottle in the holes of a wire fence. Wooley would run to the milk bottle and drink his milk. That was the way this baby got fed for about six weeks.

   Brad had a big black brush. Brad fixed a loop in a rope. He tied Wooley's bottle to the fence near the stoop. While the lamb was drinking his milk, Brad would brush Wooley's wool until it was smooth. After Wooley got done with his milk, he would back up into Brad's legs. Wooley liked to have his wool brushed smooth. Brad liked to keep Wooley looking clean.

Why did Brad take the lamb away from the herd?
What did he do with Wooley?
Why did he stop feeding him in his arms?
What did Brad do while the lamb was drinking his milk?

THE BLACK WIDOW SPIDER

The black widow spider lives near farmlands and peoples' houses. It likes cool, dark places such as cellars and sheds. It spins its messy web beneath floorboards or in piles of rubbish. Many times they live in bedrooms or bathrooms. They have also been found in some schools.

A black widow spider is shy and does not want to be disturbed. It will attack humans only when it is surprised or afraid. When it is surprised, it has venom in its teeth. The bites cause pain and muscle cramps. When a person has been bitten by a black widow spider, it is difficult for them to breathe. It is unusual for a person to die from a spider bite though. Black widow spiders are shiny-black with bright red markings shaped like an hourglass on their underside. The male black widow spider is much smaller than the female. The bite from a male black widow is less harmful because he has only a tiny amount of venom in his fangs.

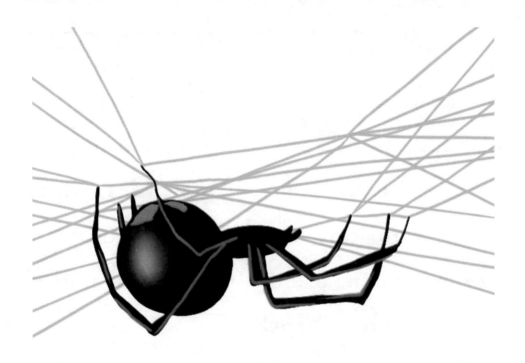

I know one thing. I would not want to put my foot on one, would you?

Where do black widow spiders like to live?
Where do they spin their webs?
When do they attack a person?
Why is it not as bad to be bitten by a male black widow spider?

POINTER, THE WATCHDOG

Mrs. Sway did not like dogs. She was not happy the day Dad brought a puppy home for his little girl, Royal. Mrs. Sway did not want any dogs around at all. At first she was in a lousy mood. She said a dog would cause trouble.

"Royal is getting to be a big girl now. She must have a dog," said Mr. Sway. "She is only four years old. This hound will sprawl all over in a short time. I do not want a dog in the house. He will grow to be too big," answered Mrs. Sway. "Oh, I want the puppy," cried Royal. "I will call him Pointer."

"I can make a dog house so Pointer can sleep outside. He and Royal can play together with her friends out in the yard or in South Park," said Mr. Sway.

Mr. Sway taught Royal how to be loving and kind with a puppy. As Pointer got older, he watched over Royal. Any time Royal was close to trouble or might be hurt,

Pointer pushed her to one side to protect her. He was her best friend.

At last, Mrs. Sway said, "I will have to say that it was a good idea to get Pointer."

What did Mr. Sway do for Royal?
Why was Mrs. Sway so mad?
What did Royal call her puppy?
What did Pointer do for Royal?

THE MUDDY POND

Betty and Sandy were playing at the pond. Sandy was looking up in the sky where the birds were building nests. One bird would fly to the pond and pick up some grass or straw. Then it would carry it back to the nest. Another one would do the same thing. They would do it over and over. This looked as if it was going to be a big nest. They made trip after trip.

Sandy said, "I get dizzy just watching them. They do not even take time out to play." Just then, Sandy slipped into the mud up to his shins. "Woops, I should be watching where I am going."

Betty said, "Can you wade over here? I can help pull you out. Oh, boy, you are muddy all over."

Sandy said, "Maybe a duck could swim here. Some fish could swim here, but I

can not even wade here. This is too
muddy for me. At least the birds can
fly over the top of this. They do not
have to walk into it."

Betty gave Sandy a hand to help pull
him out. She said, "Your hands are so
sticky and slippery I do not know if I
can hang on to you."

Sandy said, "Please help get me out. I
want to go to a lake where I can swim.
I do not want to swim in the mud."

Where did Sandy and Betty go?
What was Sandy watching?
What can swim in the pond?
Where does Sandy want to go to swim?

THE WRISTWATCH

Peggy was always late. It was hard for her to get out of bed in the morning. She was too sleepy. She did not hear the wrens and robins singing in the morning to awaken her. Often she was late for the bus. Sometimes she missed the bus and Mom had to take her to school.

Peggy was late again coming back from play at Nan's house. Mom said, "Peggy, you are late again. You are going to have to learn to tell time. I will teach you. I am going to get you a wristwatch. Then you will know how fast you have to hurry."

That day, Mom got a pretty watch for

Peggy. She put it on her wrist. "Thanks, Mom," said Peggy. "I like having a wristwatch. My watch looks good on my wrist. I will not be late anymore."

Why was Peggy late for school?
Where had she been playing when she was late coming home?
What did Mom get Peggy?
What did Mom teach Peggy to do?

A KNOCK AT THE DOOR

Jill had been sleeping. She heard a knock on the door. She tried to wake up, but she was too sleepy. Dad had lost his key and was knocking on the door. He knocked again. Still there was no answer. Dad knocked three times more.

Dad called, "Jill wake up. I lost my key. Come let me in."

At last Jill woke up from all the noise. She came to the door and turned the knob.

"Hello, Dad," Jill said. "I heard your knock at the door. Why did you not open the door? You did not need to knock."

Dad laughed, "Oh, yes, I did. I lost my key. I am glad I did not have to knock any louder to get you out of bed. Thanks, Jill. I am sorry I had to wake you."

Where was Jill when Dad knocked at the door?
Why did she not answer the knock at first?
How many more times did Dad have to knock?
Why did Dad have to knock?

CRUMBS FOR THE BIRDS

Jan said, "Winter is coming soon. Look at the birds flying away." Jan watched the birds each day. They were flying south. They wanted to get to a warmer home.

One day five birds landed on Jan's porch. "They must be hungry," she said. "I will put some crumbs out for them." She threw out three cups of crumbs. They gobbled it up fast.

Then she saw five more birds on the limb of a bare tree. Jan said, "I am going to feed them, too." She put out more crumbs and some birdseed. The

birds on the tree limbs flew to the porch.
They flapped their wings and made a
dive bomb for the food.

All ten birds had a winter feast with
Jan's crumbs and seeds.

Why were the birds flying south?
How many birds landed on Jan's porch at first?
Where did she see the other birds?
How many birds did she see in all?

A KNITTED COAT

Meg's mother liked to sew and knit. Meg used to watch her. She said, "Mom, will you teach me how to sew?"

"Sure," said Mom. "Let us get a needle and some thread. You have to learn to thread a needle first."

Meg looked at the little hole in the needle. "Mom, I have changed my mind. My thumbs get in the way when I try to thread a needle. The eye of the needle is too little. I want to learn to knit. I can learn to knit now."

Mom got some knitting needles. "This will be better for you," said

Mom. "These knitting needles do not have holes."

Meg said, "Yes, this will be better. Now I can knit a coat for my kitten. I think he would like a knitted coat made just for him. I will brush and comb his own coat and then put his new coat on him."

What did Meg want to learn to do?
What did Mom give her first?
Why did she not use it?
What did she do for her kitten?

WATCH THE SIGNS AND NEWSPAPER HEADLINES

Everywhere you go, signs and headlines are in sight for you to read.

Stop sign . . . . No right turn

Exit . . . . A light in the
lighthouse

No left turn . . . . Women

Men . . . . Sidewalk closed

Flight on Time . . . . . . Flight Delayed

Big Fight on
T.V Screen . . . . New Bank Opens

No questions are given for this story.

STOP

NEW BANK OPENS!

EXIT

BIG FIGHT!!

MEN

WOMEN

SIDEWALK CLOSED

FLIGHT ON TIME

FLIGHT DELAYED

THE BIG CATS

Princess and Knight were two of the best tigers in the circus. All of the people of Sign Creek cheered for them. Their trainer, Katy, knew just how to handle them.

Princess had been born in a zoo. The zoo was too crowded to keep her. So Katy took

Princess home when she was three weeks old. Katy knew she could train Princess to do tricks for the circus.

Knight had been born in a jungle. Sometimes he had to be watched closely. Katy was able to make him knuckle down and behave. Katy was a good trainer. Katy would crack her whip and the tigers would do their act. She had a knack for training animals.

One time Knight got off of his pathway. The crowd shouted, "There is a wild tiger on the loose!" The people started to run out of the circus tents. Some people were knocked down.

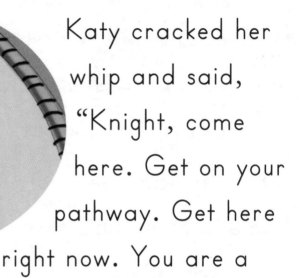

Katy cracked her whip and said, "Knight, come here. Get on your pathway. Get here right now. You are a good big cat. Let us do your act."

When Knight heard Katy talking to him, he got back on the pathway and they started their act. The excited people returned to their seats and enjoyed the circus.

Which tiger had been born in a zoo?
Who was the trainer for the tigers?
Which tiger had to be watched closely?

THE WRONG COUNT

Bob was studying for a math test. He had studied hard and wanted to do his best. He did not want to get any wrong. He was sure that three + two = five. He knew two + two = four. Bob had worked on 3 + 4. Was the answer 6 or 7? Maybe he should study a little harder. He had written the answers to the math facts many times. It helped him to write the answer to the problem again.

The day of the test came. Bob had 20 problems. There was that problem: 3 + 4. Was the answer 6 or 7? He could not remember for sure. What if he got it wrong? What if he missed another one? Should he put down 6 or 7? Bob was scared. Was he going to do well on the test?

When he got his paper back, he checked the answer to 3 + 4. The answer was 7. He did not have it wrong. It was right. Three plus four is seven. Bob did not have a single answer wrong. Bob was glad he had studied for the test.

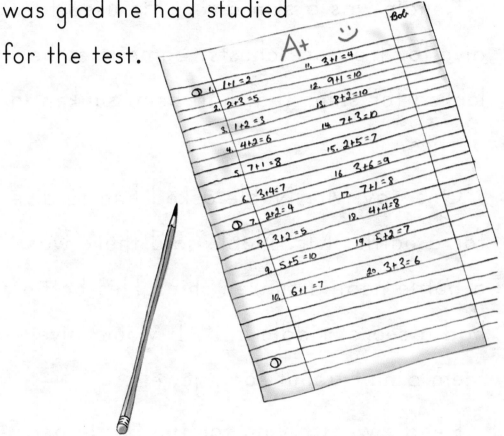

What problems did Bob know for sure?
What problem gave him trouble?
What is the answer to 3 + 4?
How did Bob do on his math test?

THE SUNKEN BOTTLE

Kendle was a skin diver. He used to dive for treasure chests. Sometimes he looked for ships that had been sunken in battles.

One day Mr. Noble asked him to dive for a bottle. Mr. Noble said there was a bottle near a sunken ship. This bottle had a secret riddle in it. It would give them a hint about some jewels.

Kendle went diving for the bottle near the sunken ship. He found things he did not want. He found a rifle and some guns. He found three silver kettles and a table.

At last, Kendle found the bottle in the king's middle cabin. Kendle gave the bottle to Mr. Noble. Inside the bottle was a note. The note said, "THE JEWELS ARE IN A CAVE BACK OF THE CASTLE."

Mr. Noble gave Kendle a bundle of money for his work. Both men became very rich after they got the jewels from the cave in back of the castle.

What kind of a job did Kendle have?
What did Mr. Noble want Kendle to do?
What did Kendle find first?
What was in the bottle?
Where did they find the jewels?

THE NEW SADDLE

Wendle was a tall man who had a big ranch. He had a horse he called "Trouble". Trouble was a beauty of a horse. He was black all over except for a little white star on his head. When Trouble was not in his stall, Wendle rode him bareback most of the time.

Trouble was a very smart horse. He would lift the handle of the barn door and let the other horses out in the yard. He could open other doors and eat the cows' food. He could jump over a wall and eat the green grass in the pasture.

When Wendle rode him, Trouble trotted in the middle of mud puddles. Wendle said, "I think Trouble needs a saddle. He might not like it at first, but I think I can get him used to it."

Wendle held out an apple to Trouble. As Trouble was eating his apple, Wendle brushed him and put the saddle blanket on his back. Then Wendle put the saddle on Trouble.

Trouble wiggled a bit. He stomped his feet. As soon as Trouble had his saddle on his back, he settled down and stood still.

Wendle said, "I think Trouble is out of trouble now."

What did Wendle call his horse?
What did Trouble do?
How did Wendle ride Trouble?
What did Wendle do to make Trouble settle down?

MR. BITTLE'S HELPER

Little Carl had a leg that was crippled. He had to walk with crutches. One leg was bent and twisted. The doctor said that Carl had to swim. He had to swim every day so he could get better.

Carl did not know how to swim but he was

not afraid of the water. Mom took him to the swimming pool every day. Mr. Bittle gave special lessons. He was very gentle with Carl and all the kids in his class. He did not want anyone to be careless and get hurt.

Carl said, "I do not want to use crutches forever. I want to learn to walk straight. I am going to work hard while I am swimming. Mr. Bittle is a good teacher. I know he can help me."

Some of the kids in the class were bigger. Some were smaller. Lots of the kids were afraid of the water. Some of the kids cried.

When one boy was crying because he could not do the sidestroke, Carl said, "Come on. Just try again. You can do it." Carl was Mr. Bittle's best helper.

Carl took lessons for a year. He got better each day. Every day his leg looked straighter.

His doctor said, "Carl, you are the greatest. You are so good you could be a part-time teacher."

The second year, Carl did not have to use crutches. He did not even limp. His leg was straight. He could play football and basketball with all the kids.

Carl said, "When I grow up, I am going to be a teacher just like Mr. Bittle. I think I will teach swimming."

Why did Carl take swimming lessons?
What was his teacher's name?
How long did he have to take swimming lessons?
What did he want to do when he was older?

SKIPPER'S NEW NAME

A letter came for Skip. Would this be the news he had been waiting to get? Would he get to swim with the team? Was he that good? Skip's heart skipped a beat.

He stood for a bit. "I think I have made the team! I have wished for it. I have prayed I would make it. Oh, I hope, I hope."

Slowly Skip opened the letter. It said, "SKIPPER FISHER. PLEASE COME TO THE SWIM MEET ON MONDAY, JUNE 10th AT 10:00 a.m. YOU ARE ON THE TEAM."

Skip did a "wowie-spin". "I made the team! I made the team!" he yelled. He could not stand still.

The team would be in a swimming contest. Slim would do the backstroke. Frank had the breaststroke. Billy was to do the sidestroke. Jack would do the crawl. They had chosen Skippper to do the fancy dives.

Everyday the boys worked out at the pool. Each day they went into their drills. They became better everyday. At last the day of the contest came. Each boy had a grin on his face. It was fun to swim in the contest.

Billy's sidestroke was just fast enough to get him in fifth place. He got a purple ribbon. Frank came in third with a red ribbon. Jack and Slim each got a white ribbon for second place.

Then it was time for Skip to do his dives. He did high dives. He did a low dive, slow dive. He did dives with a twist. Then he did his best dive. It was a circle flip right into the water.

Everyone yelled, "Bravo! Bravo! Good dives, Skipper!"

Skip won first place with a gold ribbon. The judge said, "Here is to Skipper Fisher. He is our best flipper."

After that, everyone called Skip, "Skipper Flipper". Skip liked his new name.

How did Skip find out that he was on the team?
What did Skip do in the contest?
What did he win in the contest?
How did they change his name?

JUDD'S SURPRISE FOR DAD

Judd's dad had a big blue truck. His name was on the door. Dad kept his truck spick and span. He used to brag about what a good truck he had.

Buck and Russ were Judd's pals. Dad often took all three of the boys with him in his truck. Dad said, "This will be a trip to the garbage dump," he said. "There will be lots of mud puddles and dust. Are you sure you want to go?"

Judd and the other boys agreed. They wanted to go to with him. The truck had to go through slush and mud. They were in dirt up to the hubcaps. Mud was splashed all over the truck.

The boys saw trash that was crushed. Junk and scraps were everywhere. The dump was a mess. They dumped out their scraps and trash. They were glad to rush out of there.

As soon as Dad got home, he went in the house. Judd said, "Let us surprise Dad. This truck is a mess. Let us get a brush and scrub it up so it is spick and span."

All three of the boys got to work. They began to scrub and scrub. They waxed the truck. It was a beautiful job.

Dad came out and said, "What a beautiful job you boys did on the truck. I am proud of you. How would you like to go out and get some hamburgers now?" That was a surprise for the boys, but they all said, "Yes!"

How did Judd's dad usually keep his truck?
Where did he take the boys?
What happened to the truck at the dump?
What did the boys do to surprise Dad?
What did Dad do to surprise the boys?

SILLY FARMER TALLMAN

Farmer Tallman put the rain boots on his hands. The moon was shining all day and it was hot.

He went to the house to feed the sheep. The sheep said, "Moo, Moo."

After that, Farmer Tallman went to the bedroom to meet the goats. He put a saddle on a goat and rode the goat to the chicken house. He wanted to see if the chickens had any milk for him.

He said, "I will go see if the donkey has any eggs for my dinner."

Farmer Tallman's wife fixed him one dozen toasted eggs and made him some

fried toast. When he had finished his breakfast, he drove to the bakery to get a haircut and shave.

At sunrise, Farmer Tallman put on his pajamas and went to sleep. He had a full day's work and was wide awake.

Can you read this story again and change it so it is not silly?

Where should Farmer Tallman have put his rain boots?

What animal says "Moo, Moo"?

Where should he have put a saddle?

Which animals give milk?

What do chickens do?

Did you ever eat toasted eggs and fried toast?

What do you buy at a bakery?

At what time do you go to bed?

THE WRESTLERS

Frank and Eric were going to high school. They both were good at playing football. They were on the basketball team. Each year they kept trying to see who could make the most home runs at the baseball games.

Both Eric and Andy wanted to learn wrestling. The school did not have a team, so they watched wrestling on TV. "We need a wrestling coach," said Eric.

Frank had an idea. "My Uncle Joe used to be a wrestling coach. I will write to him and see if he could teach us to wrestle."

Dear Uncle Joe,

Eric and I want to learn to wrestle. We would like to have you teach us. We know you are busy. Can we help you at the garage? I could help fix the cars. I am good at handling all the tools. Eric said he could be wrapping all the parts and sending them out. He said he would sweep all the floors, too.

Please write to us and let us know if you could teach us wrestling.

We love you,
Frank

Uncle Joe got the letter Frank had written. He wrote a letter back. The letter said:

Dear Frank,

It is a deal. I will teach you wrestling. You can handle my new wrenches that I use when I am fixing the wrecked cars.

Love,

Uncle Joe

Eric and Frank learned to be good wrestlers. Uncle Joe had good help fixing the wrecked cars in his garage.

What kind of sports did Eric and Frank like?
What did they want to learn to do?
What could they do for Uncle Joe?
What could Uncle Joe do for them?

THE DANCING
ELEPHANTS

Cecil and Casper were two small circus elephants. Cecil was very smart. He could be trained to do some circus acts.

Carl was their trainer. He was teaching them how to dance. It was a cinch to teach Cecil. He caught on fast. Teaching Casper was another thing. He was slow to learn to dance.

Cecil seemed to love music. He would dance and prance in

time to the music. Casper glanced
down at his own feet. He watched
Cecil dance and prance. Casper
just could not dance. He just
marched up and down.

At last, Bob said, "Casper, we are going to let you lead the parade. You can march in front with your big feet, one step at a time. Cecil will do the dancing."

What were Cecil and Casper?
Which elephant was smarter?
What did Cecil learn to do?
What was Casper's job going to be with the circus?

THE GIANT

Gene was a giant who did an act for the carnival on the stage. He took giant steps across the path where the crowd was sitting. Everyone clapped for the giant. He had huge feet and put them in huge shoes. His arms and legs were huge, too. He was a giant, but he was a gentle giant. Everyone loved Gene.

Sometimes Gene would walk in with a giraffe. He had taught the giraffe how to bow to the people. Gene said, "You think I am a giant. Just look at this giraffe. He is the giant. I am a midget beside the giraffe." The giraffe had a long, long neck, and very long legs. He did look like a giant beside Gene.

Greg was in charge of getting food for the giant. Greg got some meat, vegetables, bread and milk. He fixed a nice dinner for Gene. Marge was a midget in the carnival. She often had dinner with Gene. After she ate her meal, she said, "What about a dessert? I think I will fix a gelatin dessert for Gene."

Gene said "That is exactly what I have been wanting. I would like a cherry gelatin dessert with lots of fruit. You had a good idea, Marge."

What size was Gene?
What animal did Gene bring on the stage?
What size was Marge?
What did Marge fix for Gene to eat?

A HOSPITAL FOR VANCE

Vance did not like being in the hospital. He was going to have to be there for three days. Three days seemed like a century to him. He began to pout. He would not eat his lunch. He threw celery at the nurses. He would not even eat the ginger cookies they

brought him. He acted like a spoiled kid.
He was in a rage.

The nurses wanted to give him a
chance, but they did not know what to do.
They were very gentle with him. Dr. Race
came in to talk to him. He said, "Vance,
you are just being naughty and you know
it. This will have to cease. We want to
help you get well. There is a circus coming
to town and we want you to be well so you
can see it. You will have to help us. Can
we call it a truce?"

Vance was not very proud of himself.
He said, "Sorry, Dr. Race. I will try."

The next day was better. He did not throw his celery at the nurses. He ate all his meals. He did not pout and act naughty. He was certain he could be good.

The nurses gave him a special treat of a cinnamon roll. He ate all the citrus fruit. He said, "I feel better already. I want to get well so I can go to the circus. That will be fun."

How long did Vance have to stay in the hospital?
How did he act at first?
Who told him about the circus?
What did Vance decide to do about getting well?

ELEPHANTS

Elephants are very intelligent animals. People have used them as a way of travel for thousands of years. They also used them as we use wagons, cars or trains. Now we just see them at a zoo or circus.

An elephant can walk faster than a man can walk. A herd of elephants on the march can cover a distance of 50 miles in one day.

Elephants will eat up to 500 pounds of food in one day. They eat green leaves, fruit and plant shoots. They drink about 40 gallons of water at a time. If an elephant's trunk is hurt, it can starve to death.

The elephant is a good swimmer. He loves the water and sometimes uses his trunk for a snorkel.

These huge beasts have a way of

talking to each other by making rumbling
noises that sound like gargling. When an
elephant thinks there is danger, it will
alert others by stopping the noise.

The largest tusk ever found was 10 feet long and weighed over 230 pounds.

Elephants keep their families together. Their family ties are very close. If a member of their family dies, they cover the body with twigs and leaves. They grieve by standing beside the grave for many hours. When they are unhappy, they cry like humans.

How did people used to use elephants?
How much can an elephant eat in one day?
How many gallons of water does he drink?
How do they talk to each other?

THE MONARCH BUTTERFLY

The monarch butterfly is one of the most beautiful of all butterflies. It is an insect with six legs and a body divided into three parts. Butterflies have wings and feelers. These feelers are slender and have knobs on the end. Butterflies rest with their wings together. The bright color shows on both sides of the wings.

These beautiful butterflies have paper-thin wings. The wings have black and white stripes with yellow spots. Their bright color shows that they are unpleasant or poisonous to eat. The caterpillars feed on milkweed and their bodies take the poison from the milkweed.

About 5 million monarch butterflies from North America fly to cities along the coast of California where it is warmer. This way the caterpillars will not freeze in the cold climate of the north. Monarch butterflies can fly over 3000 miles. Sometimes they fly as far as 80 miles in one day.

How many legs do insects have?
What do the monarch caterpillars eat?
Where do the monarch butterflies go for the winter?
How many miles can they fly in one day?

JAKE'S PAPER ROUTE

Jake had a paper route with 49 papers to deliver. He had to get up at 4:30 every morning so he could get the papers to the houses before 6:00 A.M. It was important for Jake to get plenty of sleep.

One night he had stayed up very late watching T.V. When it came time to get up the next morning, he was sleepy. The snooze alarm rang twice. Finally Jake pulled himself out of bed and got dressed.

Where were his shoes? He couldn't find them. For a minute he went wild! No way could he go on his paper route without shoes. "Oh, great! I remember now. I left them in the living room where I had been watching T.V."

He was so sleepy that he forgot to take his address list with him. "Oh, well," he said, "I think I can remember all the houses." He was nearly finished with his route when he saw he had an extra paper. "Where is the house I missed?" he grumbled. "I can't find it."

Jake hurried back to his house to get his address list. When he got to his front porch, he said, "Oh, great! Now I find it. It was my own house that I forgot. I think I was too sleepy to THINK! I think I better watch my bedtime from now on."

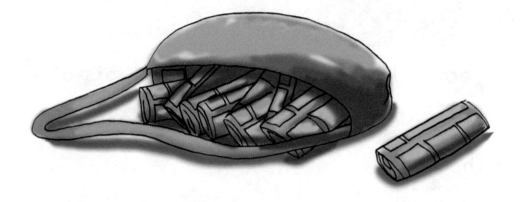

What kind of a job did Jake have?
What time did he have to get up in the morning?
What had he forgotten to take with him on his route?
What did he find out when he had one paper left over?

RODNEY'S JOBS

Rodney was a twelve-year old boy. He was the oldest child in a family of three boys. The twin boys were only three years old. Mom had to spend lots of her time cooking and taking care of the twins.

Rodney did most of the extra chores to help Mom. Everyday he would walk the dog, Sparky. The twins liked to play with Sparky, but they were too little to take a walk with him alone.

There were two big, lazy cats that the family loved. Rodney was the one who fed them and kept their bed clean. Whenever Rodney sat down, the cats were in his lap.

Rodney's best job was taking care of Pacer, his pet colt. Pacer was only a month old when Rodney got him. Rodney put the hay in his manger and saw to it that Pacer had fresh water. Each day when Rodney came home from school, Pacer would walk across the yard to meet him.

How old was Rodney?
How old were his little brothers?
What did Rodney do for Sparky and the cats?
What was Rodney's best job?